Published by Coordination Group Publications Ltd

Written by:
Lynn Howard
Barbara Mascetti
With graphics by:
Barking Dog Art
Typesetting, design and graphics by:
Victoria Brereton, Martin Chester, Glenn Rogers,
Alice Shepperson, Sharon Watson, Chrissy Williams

With thanks to Taissa Csáky for the proofreading.

ISBN: 978 1 84146 350 6
Groovy Website: www.cgpbooks.co.uk

Printed by Elanders Hindson Ltd, Newcastle upon Tyne.
Jolly bits of clipart from CorelDRAW®.

Contents

Invasion and Settlement

Britain has been invaded many times in the past.

Many of the invaders decided to settle here, including the Romans.

People often <u>choose</u> to settle in another place, but sometimes they have <u>no choice</u>.

1 | Put the "reasons for moving" below into the table.

There was a war in our village, so we had to move to somewhere safer.

We moved nearer to the best school in the area, so we could send our daughter there.

I lost my job, so I had to move to a place where I could get a new job.

We wanted to live in the countryside, so we moved out of the city.

Choosing to move house	Forced to move house
	There was a war in our village, so we had to move to somewhere safer.

2 | Draw lines to match the beginnings of these sentences to their endings.

1. Invasion is...   .....moving away from where you were born.

2. Settlement is...   .....arriving at an area and attacking it.

3. Emigration is...   .....staying in an area for a long time.

3 | In the boxes next to each word below, write an 'i' if they are to do with invasion, and an 's' if they are to do with settlement.

☐ Armour   ☐ Farming   ☐ Stay

☐ Home   ☐ War   ☐ Conquest

Many people are still forced to leave their homes today, because of war.
Can you think of places in the world where this is happening today?

The Celts

Before the Romans came, people called Celts lived in Britain.

1 | Draw lines to match up these sentences about Celts and Romans. Then write 'S' for same or 'D' for different on the dotted lines.

The Romans

They spoke Latin.
They were ruled by one Emperor.
They worshipped many gods.
The men all shaved.
They wore tunics.
Many Romans lived in towns.

The Celts

They had many kings. .....
They worshipped many gods. .....
The men wore moustaches. .....
They wore trousers. .....
They did not have towns. .....
They spoke a language similar to Welsh. .D..

2 | Is this picture of a Celt or a Roman? Give reasons.

Answer — ....

Reasons — ....

....

3 | The Romans and Celts fought very differently. Who is more likely to say these things?

Write **R** for **Roman Soldier**, or **C** for **Celtic Warrior**.

"Our soldiers join the army for 20 years." **R**

"Our army is split up into different legions." .....

"The king is pleased when we win battles." .....

4 | Circle <u>three</u> things below that the Celts were famous for.

POETRY   MAKING SOFAS   METALWORK

VOLLEY BALL   JEWELLERY   SPEAKING LATIN   SPACE TRAVEL

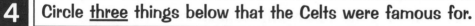

Celtic jewellery was very beautiful. People still wear it today.

The Romans

The Roman army was pretty scary, and more organised than a march into assembly.

1 **Use words from the box below to label the diagram, showing different bits of a Roman Soldier's battle costume.**

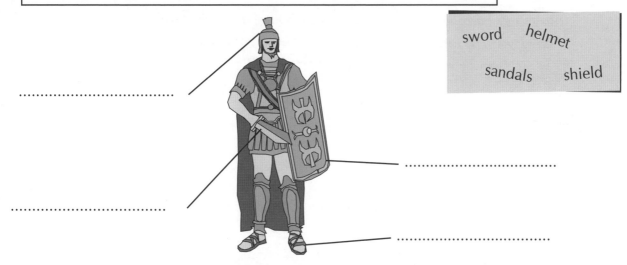

sword   helmet   sandals   shield

....

....

....

....

2 **The Roman Army was split into different parts. Draw lines to match up the start of each sentence with the right ending.**

1. The Roman Army was split into different...   ...of 60 centuries.

2. There were about 30 legions...   ...contained about 80 men.

3. Each legion was made up...   ...sections called legions.

4. One century...   ...in the whole Empire.

3 **When the Romans invaded Britain, they had a bit of trouble to start with. Fill in the blanks using words from the box.**

France   55BC

Claudius   Britons

400   Romans

The Romans first invaded England in ....

The .... fought fiercely and drove them back.

The .... invaded again one year later.

This time they beat the Britons, but then had to go to .... to fight off a rebellion.

The Emperor .... finally invaded properly almost 100 years later in AD43.

This time the Romans were here to stay, and ruled England for nearly .... years.

ACTIVITY: _Draw a picture of a **Celtic Warrior** and a **Roman Soldier**._
Put labels on your picture to show how they are different.

Boudicca

Boudicca was a British tribal queen who revolted against the Romans in AD 60.

1 **Read the passage below and answer the questions.**

> Boudicca's husband was the leader of the rich Iceni tribe. He thought his family would be safe if he gave in to the Romans. But when he died, the Romans wanted all the fortune he had left to Boudicca.

a) What was the name of Boudicca's tribe?

....

Find out the full story of Boudicca from books or the Internet.

b) Why did Boudicca's husband give in to the Romans?

....

c) What happened when Boudicca's husband died?

....

2 **Can you put these sentences about Boudicca into the correct order?**

A The Roman army finally defeated Boudicca.
She poisoned herself rather than be captured.

B The Romans had Boudicca flogged.

(flogged = very badly beaten)

C In revenge for the flogging, Boudicca's army attacked the Roman towns and killed thousands of Romans.

The correct order is ☐ , ☐ , ☐ .

EXTRA ACTIVITY:

You'll need to find out some more information about Boudicca before you do this activity.

1. Imagine you are a <u>British survivor</u> of Boudicca's revolt.
What would you think Boudicca was like? Write a short passage about her.
*(Hint: Do you think she was **good** or **bad**? Was she **brave** or **stupid**?)*

2. Now imagine you are a <u>Roman survivor</u> of the revolt. Write another passage about her.
*(Hint: Would you think she was **brave** or **stupid**? Was she a **heroine** or an **evil rebel**?)*

Roman Baths

The Romans bathed in a very special way. They followed a long process to get clean.

1 **Fill in the blanks using words in the box to explain how a hypocaust system worked.**

| floor   pillars |
| wood-burning furnace |
| central heating |

Hypocaust systems were a bit like ....

A .... was built under the floor. It sent hot air up

through the .... and gaps in the walls. The floor was held up by lots

of .... , so the hot air could spread everywhere.

2 **Label the diagram of Roman baths below using words in the box.**

hypocaust   cold pool   warm room
changing room   hot steam room

3
....
(where people got clean by rubbing oil into their skin then sweating it all out)

4
....
(people would jump into this right at the end to close up the pores of their skin)

2
....
....
(people went here after getting undressed)

1
....
....
(people started off in here)

5
....
(this is how the floors, water and hot rooms got heated up)

Ooh, there's nothing nicer than a hot, steamy bath. The Romans certainly thought so...

The Anglo-Saxons

After the Romans left, the Anglo-Saxons started to make raids on Britain.
During the fifth century AD they took over much of the country.

1 | **Complete the labels on the map using the words below.**

| Eastern Britain | Saxony | Denmark |

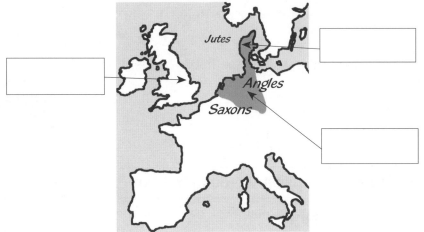

The shaded bit shows where the Anglo-Saxons came from.

The Anglo-Saxons were made up of **three tribes** — the Angles, the Saxons and the Jutes.

2 | **Use the underlined words in the passage to complete the sentences underneath.**

> The Anglo-Saxons were not peaceful when they moved into Britain as <u>migrants</u>.
> They started off as <u>raiders</u> of Britain and gradually became <u>invaders</u>, then <u>settlers</u>.
> Many of the British had to flee to Wales as <u>refugees</u>.

Ra .... take part in a surprise attack, often to steal.

M *igrants* .... go to a new country to live there permanently.

R .... have to flee their own country because of danger.

S .... go to a country to live there permanently.

I .... enter another country as enemies, intending to conquer it.

3 | **Put the five words from question 2 into the correct circles below.**

<u>Warlike</u>   <u>Normally Peaceful</u>

raiders

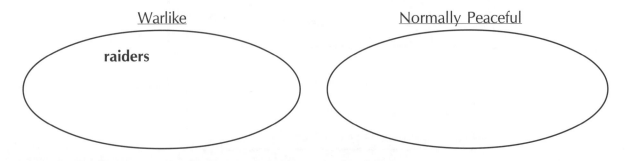

The word "England" comes originally from the words "Angle-land."

Anglo-Saxon Life

The Anglo-Saxons didn't live in towns like the Romans.
They lived in wooden houses in small farming villages.

1 Below are some <u>facts</u> about Anglo-Saxons and <u>reasons</u> which explain each fact. Can you match them up?

Fact about Anglo-Saxons:

Fact 1:
They did not make many grand buildings,
but they did sometimes build churches.

Fact 2:
People lived in houses made of
wood, clay and sticks.

Fact 3:
Most villages had two large fields
on either side of the village,
shared out into strips for each family.

Fact 4:
Once, there were several Anglo-Saxon
kingdoms. Later, they became one kingdom.

Reason we know this:

Reason A:
From an aeroplane you can
still see the pattern of the fields.

Reason B:
We have books written at the
time by Christian monks about
the Anglo-Saxon kingdoms.

Reason C:
Some Anglo-Saxon churches
are still standing.

Reason D:
Archaeologists have dug up the remains
of Anglo-Saxon villages and farms.

Fact 1 goes with reason **C** ....
Fact 2 goes with reason ....

Fact 3 goes with reason ....
Fact 4 goes with reason ....

2 At first, the Anglo-Saxons worshipped many gods. Later they became Christians. Write down two clues which tell you they were Christians.

1. ....

Hint — look at the "reasons" from Q1

2. ....

ACTIVITY:

Here is a picture of an Anglo-Saxon man.
Draw your own picture of an Anglo-Saxon man.

Label these things on your picture:
tunic, purse, leggings, cloak.

Section Two — The Anglo-Saxons

Archaeology

Archaeologists study the past by finding things <u>buried in the ground</u>.

Historians study the past by looking at <u>written records</u>.

1 | **Who would study each of these things?**
Write "A" for Archaeologist or "H" for Historian.

1. Traces of old buildings ....

5. Diaries ....

2. Old letters .....**H**.......

6. Chips of flint ....

3. Wills ....

7. Jewellery ....

4. Broken pottery ....

8. Old rubbish heaps ....

2 | **Put the words below into the passage about archaeology.**

| LAYERS | SURVEY | TROWELS | FINDS | EXCAVATION |

You can't dig everywhere. So you do a .... to see where would be a likely

place to make interesting .... An aerial survey can show things invisible

when you're on the ground. But the actual .... isn't so easy.

Working by hand using ...., the archaeologists carefully remove

the .... of earth and rock.

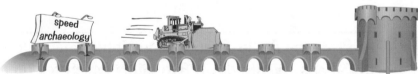

3 | Pete is an archaeologist. He finds the remains of an old house buried in the ground.
He digs further down and finds the foundations of a fort.
Which do you think was built first? The house or the fort? Can you explain why?

....

....

ACTIVITY:

It is the Year 3000. Henry is an archaeologist of the future.
Make a list of things that Henry <u>might find</u> if he digs where your town used to be.
Make a list of things that he <u>probably won't find</u> because they won't last that long.

Sutton Hoo

In 1939 the tomb of an Anglo-Saxon king was discovered at Sutton Hoo in Suffolk.
It was full of precious artefacts, but the most amazing thing was that the tomb was inside a buried ship.

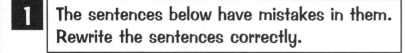

The pictures to the right show two artefacts found at Sutton Hoo.

1 | **The sentences below have mistakes in them. Rewrite the sentences correctly.**

The pictures show a <u>spear</u> and a helmet.

....

They were found at <u>Hutton Soo</u>.

....

They are made of <u>paper</u>.

....

Anglo-Saxon <u>men</u> did not fight, so they must have belonged to a <u>woman</u>.

....

2 | <u>Draw lines</u> **to match the things below to what they tell us about Anglo-Saxon life.**

Things found in the Sutton Hoo

Musical instruments and jewellery.

A sceptre (a staff).

Some Christian symbols — like a cross.
(Ship burial is not usually a Christian custom.)

What they tell us

Anglo-Saxon life was not all war and fighting.

At that time England was partly Christian and partly not.

The dead person was a king.

3 | **One thing was missing from the tomb – a body. Which explanation below is the more likely reason for this?**

A Maybe the king was really killed in battle or lost at sea, and this grave is just a symbol.

B Maybe a hungry dog found the body and ate it.

The correct answer is ....

Knock Knock. Who's there? Sutton. Sutton who? That's right, Sutton Hoo.

Viking Invaders

The Vikings came from Scandinavia — that's the countries we call Denmark, Norway and Sweden today.

1 **Look at the map to the right.**

Colour in **Britain** in one colour and label it "Britain".

Colour in the countries that the **Vikings came from** in another colour.

2 **People invade countries for many reasons.**
Listed below are possible reasons why the Vikings invaded England.
Tick the correct reasons.

☐ England had good weather and soil for growing crops.

☐ The Vikings were bored of having pointy hats.

☐ Scandinavia was very cold and had poor soil for growing crops.

☐ The English kept fighting the Romans.

☐ The Vikings wanted to join the Eurovision Song Contest.

☐ England had weak defences.

3 **Read the information below.**

First the Vikings attacked England and then went away.
Later they decided to stay and built their own towns such as Yorvik.

Complete the sentences below using these words: **Yorvik**   **raids**   **Danelaw**

1. The Vikings started to attack England by making ....

2. The Vikings settled in an area in Northern England called ....

3. The capital of this area was at York, which the Vikings called ....

ACTIVITY — WHAT WERE THE VIKINGS LIKE?

Use books or the Internet to answer these questions:

What did the Vikings look like? Find pictures of them.
What weapons did they use? What other names were the Vikings known by?

Viking Longboats

The Vikings sailed in huge, fast ships called longboats.

1 | Label the diagram of the longboat below using the words in the circle.

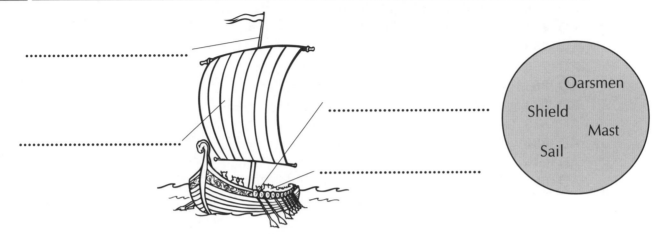

Oarsmen

Shield

Mast

Sail

They raided England without warning. They slaughtered, burned and robbed people.

2 | Complete the paragraph below using the words in the box.

rivers   monasteries   longboats

The Vikings came across the North Sea in their ....

They sailed up the English .... They attacked the English

.... first as they were easy targets.

3 | Are the sentences below true or false? Write **T** or **F** in the boxes.

1. The Vikings attacked English monasteries because they were rich.

2. The Vikings found their way to England by following the smell of frying bacon.

3. The English were easy to beat up as they all wore open-toed sandals.

4. The Vikings landed first on the South coast because it was closer to where they had come from.

5. The Vikings sailed up rivers to attack settlements inland.

The Vikings were great sailors in their fancy longboats. They even sailed to America.

When the Vikings Invaded

In the 1000 years before the Battle of Hastings, Britain was invaded by many different people.

AD 43	Romans **invade** England.
AD 400	Anglo-Saxons **invade** Britain.
AD 410	Romans **driven out** of Britain.
AD 787	Vikings first **visit** Britain.
AD 793	Vikings **raid** the **monastery** on Lindisfarne.
AD 865	A great army of Vikings **invade** England.
AD 871	**Alfred the Great** becomes **King** of Wessex.
AD 878	Alfred **beats** the Vikings at the Battle of Eddington.
AD 886	Alfred and the Vikings agree to **split** the country between them.
AD1016	Viking King Knut **rules** the whole of England.
AD1066	The Normans **invade** and **win** at the Battle of Hastings and begin to **rule** England.

1 Look at the timeline above. Which four groups of people invaded Britain between AD43 and AD1066?

1. ....   2. ....

3. ....   4. ....

2 Draw lines to match the dates to the Viking events.

AD865   Vikings first visit Britain.

AD793   Vikings raid Lindisfarne monastery.

AD787   Viking armies invade Britain.

3 Fill in the following table using dates from the timeline.

	Invaded	left or conquered
Romans		
Anglo-Saxons		AD1066
Vikings		AD1066
Normans	AD1066	

Britain must have had a lot to offer if so many people wanted to invade it.

Raiding Monasteries

When the Vikings invaded Britain in AD790 they attacked many monasteries, stole all the treasure and killed or captured the monks.

1 In the 790s, the monks were some of the only people who were educated. Which of these would the monks do as part of their daily lives?

Tick the correct answers.

☐ Go shopping   ☐ Have parties   ☐ Teach others

☐ Read books   ☐ Write books   ☐ Steal cars

2 Below are possible reasons why the Vikings attacked the monasteries. Write <u>true</u> or <u>false</u> next to each one.

The monasteries were full of gold and silver. ....*true*....

The Vikings wanted to play football with the monks. ....

The monks were peaceful men and would not fight back. ....

There were no armies around to defend the monks. ....

The monks laughed at the Vikings' boats. ....

The monks could be captured and sold as slaves. ....

The Vikings did not like the monks' habits (clothes). ....

The monasteries were full of valuable treasures and decorations.

3 Draw a Viking hat around items that the Vikings would have stolen from the monasteries.

like this

Basketballs   Silver

Tapestries

Longboats   Televisions

Elephants   Gold

Not even the monks and monasteries were safe from the Vikings.

Alfred the Great

King Alfred the Great was one of the greatest kings to rule in history. He was born in Berkshire in AD849 and at the age of 22 became King of Wessex.

1 **Below is a list of some of the great things that Alfred did when he was King. Copy each thing into the correct column of the table.**

built lots of forts   built a new navy

built a new army   made new laws

invented new coins   opened schools for children

fought bravely in battles   translated books from Latin

To protect people from invading armies	To make everyday life easier

2 **Name three things that Alfred the Great built while he was King.**

1. ....   2. ....   3. ....

3 **Why do you think Alfred was known as Alfred the Great? Circle the right reason below.**

He was quite tall.   He did many great things whilst he was King.   He ate lots of frosties.

ACTIVITY — THE GREATEST BRITON.

My friend Paul thinks that H from Steps is the greatest Briton of all time.

Write an argument to persuade Paul that King Alfred was greater than H.
You can use information from <u>this page</u> and from <u>page 14</u> to help you.
Or you could use <u>books and the Internet</u> to find out more.

Henry VIII

Henry VIII came to the throne in 1509, aged 18. He was a bit of a mean bully but was pretty intelligent.

1 **What kind of man was Henry VIII?**
Put a ring around the three words that describe him best.

Shy	Kind
Powerful	Selfish
Clever	Thoughtful

2 **Look at the table and answer the questions below.**

Queen	Wife Number	Children	Fate
Catherine of Aragon	1	Mary (girl)	Divorced
Anne Boleyn	2	Elizabeth (girl)	Executed
Jane Seymour	3	Edward (boy — weak and frail)	Died after childbirth
Anne of Cleves	4	None	Divorced
Catherine Howard	5	None	Executed
Catherine Parr	6	None	Outlived Henry

a) How many times did Henry VIII get married?

....

b) Did he have any healthy sons?

....

c) Why do you think Henry kept getting married?

....

ACTIVITY

Use books or the Internet to answer these questions:

What sort of clothes did Henry VIII wear?
What would the inside of his palaces have looked like?

Henry the Monarch

A group of important men lived with Henry VIII in his palaces to help him rule England. They were known as the Court.

1 | **Read the following passage about Henry VIII then answer the questions below.**

As a young man Henry let his counsellors rule the country, while he had lots of fun hunting, dancing and entertaining. But as he got older he took control of everything. He became very greedy, trusted no one, beheaded those who did not agree with him and made himself very unpopular.

a) Who ruled the country when Henry was a young king?

....

b) How did Henry change as he got older?

....

....

2 | **Put a ring around the things Henry VIII did as king.**

woodcutting   hunting   cooking   farming

ruling   producing an heir   making money   blacksmithing

3 | **Draw a line linking each of these words to its meaning.**

Monarch   a person who is part of the Court

Courtier   all those involved in ruling a country

Tyrant   a cruel and unkind ruler

Court   a ruler with the title King or Queen

Being King is not all parties, sports and fun. So there.

Henry's Divorce

Henry decided to divorce his first wife Catherine, after being married for 18 years.

1 **Are the sentences below true or false? Write T or F in each box.**

Henry wanted to be able to go shopping without Catherine nagging him. ☐

Henry had fallen in love with Anne Boleyn. ☐

Catherine of Aragon had spent all Henry's money on cheese. ☐

Catherine gave birth to a daughter but no sons. ☐

Catherine smelt of cheese. ☐

2 **Draw a line to match Henry's problems with his solutions.**

Problems:

Catherine of Aragon gave him no sons so he...

Henry wanted to divorce his wife so he...

Henry needed more money so he...

Solutions:

...broke away from the Catholic Church, as they did not agree with divorce.

...closed down the monasteries and sold all the land.

...married five more times in the hope that one wife would have a son.

Henry wanted a son to rule after him because he thought England would be weak without a King to rule.

I can't help it ... sniff sniff... I get so lonely...

3 **Jane Seymour gave Henry a son, Edward, who was quite weak. Give two reasons why Henry got married again after Jane died.**

1. ....

2. ....

Catherine of Aragon was first, then Anne Boleyn, then Jane Seymour... It's very confusing.

The End of the Monasteries

After his break with the Catholic Church, Henry VIII decided to close all the monasteries to make some money.

1 | **Put a tick next to the reasons why Henry VIII ran out of money.**

entertaining the court ☐

giving it to charity ☐

decorating his palaces ☐

spending it on cars ☐

fighting wars ☐

having BBQ pool parties ☐

2 | **Put these statements in the right order.**

1. Henry made lots of money.

2. Henry closed all the monasteries.

3. Henry VIII broke away from the Catholic Church.

4. Henry sold all their land.

Correct order is ☐ , ☐ , ☐ , ☐ .

3 | **Henry needed a proper reason to close the monasteries.**
Decide which of these statements is true and write "true" after it.

a) Henry said the monks spent all day playing board games. ....

b) Henry said the monks were lazy and were not following the monastery rules. ....

c) Henry said the monks were secret pirates. ....

Not even the monasteries were safe from Henry VIII...

Henry's Other Wives

After his divorce from Catherine of Aragon, Henry married Anne Boleyn.

When she did not give him a son he had her executed and he married Jane Seymour.

1 **Read the information below about Anne Boleyn and answer the questions.**

Anne Boleyn was a lady-in-waiting.

Henry had already fallen in love with her before he divorced Catherine of Aragon.
Anne gave Henry a daughter, Elizabeth, but he still wanted a son to rule the country
after he died.

Even though Henry loved Anne at first, she was not a popular Queen.
After a while Henry got tired of Anne and accused her of having an affair.
She was tried in court, found guilty and beheaded.

ANNE BOLEYN

a) What was Anne's job? ....

b) Was Anne a popular Queen? ....

c) What did Henry do when he got tired of Anne? ....

....

2 **Read the following passage about Jane Seymour and answer the questions.**

Eleven days after Anne's death, Henry married Jane Seymour.
She was quiet and did as she was told, unlike Anne Boleyn.
Everyone liked Jane.

Jane became pregnant very soon after the wedding and had a son, Edward.
Henry now had an heir. Jane died twelve days after the birth, and for the
first time Henry was sad about losing one of his wives.

a) Why was Jane a popular queen? ....

....

b) Did Jane have a son or a daughter? ....

Henry certainly knew what he wanted in life — and he knew how to get it.

Even More Wives

Henry married three more times before he died. His fourth wife was Anne of Cleves, his fifth Catherine Howard (who was unfaithful to him), and his sixth was Catherine Parr.

1 Fill in the blanks in the passage below, using the words in the box.

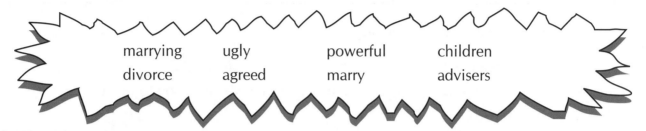

marrying   ugly   powerful   children
divorce   agreed   marry   advisers

After Jane's death, one of Henry's _____ suggested that Henry could _____ a German princess called Anne of Cleves. That way England and Germany could work together to become very _____.

Henry _____ to marry Anne even though he had only seen a painting of her. When Anne arrived, Henry saw that she was very _____.

He wanted to get out of _____ her, but he could not break his promise to her family. Henry was forced to marry her, but could _____ her quickly as she gave him no _____.

2 Henry's fifth wife Catherine Howard was young and exciting.
Henry started having some fun again.
Put a ring around the 4 things Henry and Catherine would have done.

partying   dancing   ironing   feasting

fighting   singing   gardening   washing

CATHERINE HOWARD

3 Draw a line to match each Queen with what happened to her.

Wife 4 — Anne of Cleves   executed for adultery

Wife 5 — Catherine Howard   outlived Henry

Wife 6 — Catherine Parr   divorced for having no children

Henry was a powerful man, but he still couldn't get what he really wanted — a healthy son.

Section Four — Henry VIII

Rich and Poor

Rich and poor people lived very different lives in Tudor times.

1 Look at these pictures.
Under each one, write whether you
think it is a rich man or a poor man.

a) ....   b) ....

2 Below is a list of names of people's positions in Tudor society.
Write each name next to the correct description.

NOBLE	~~YEOMAN~~	~~VAGABOND~~
MERCHANT	MONARCH	PEASANT

1. .... — King or Queen who ruled the country by God's will.

2. .... — an Earl, Duke, Lord or other aristocrat

3. .... — a trader who might become very rich

4. YEOMAN — a well-off farmer who owned land

5. .... — a poor farm worker who did not own land

6. VAGABOND — a beggar who travelled from place to place

3 Rich children and poor children were taught very different things.
Look at this table then answer the questions underneath it.

	RICH	POOR
BOYS	READING, LATIN, PUBLIC SPEAKING, MUSIC, DANCING	PRACTICAL SKILLS LIKE WOODWORK, A LITTLE READING
GIRLS	READING, MUSIC, EMBROIDERY, DANCING	COOKING AND SEWING

a) Which language did rich boys learn at school? ....

b) Were rich girls taught to read? ....

c) What were poor girls taught? ....

Advisers to Tudor Kings and Queens could become rich and powerful even if they weren't nobles.

Tudor Houses

Thanks to their strong timber frames many Tudor houses are still standing today.

1 | **Below is a list of different things that a Tudor house might have. Write each one into the correct side of the table.**

~~Large kitchen, with space for many cooks~~   tiny rooms

very small garden for vegetables only   extra rooms for servants to live in

big fireplace   no glass in the windows

flowers in the garden as well as vegetables and herbs   toilets

Poor Houses	Rich Houses
	large kitchen, with space for many cooks

2 | **Below are two lists. The first list shows some things that changed in Tudor times. Draw lines to link each change with the effect it had on rich people's houses.**

Changes in Tudor Life

Carpets from Turkey became popular.

Glass was imported from Venice.

There were fewer trees around.

Changes in houses

Timber gradually gave way to brick.

People stopped using rush matting on the floor.

There were more glass windows
in rich and middle-class houses.

3 | **Look at the question above.
Give three reasons why new Tudor houses were warmer than older houses.**

1. ....

2. ....

3. ....

Many Tudor poor people were servants and would have lived at their master's house.

What People Owned

An <u>inventory</u> is a list of things a person owns. In Tudor times, after someone died, an inventory would be made of all his or her possessions.

1 **Look at the following inventory of my friend Sharon's bedroom. In the space, write the item that shows what one of her hobbies is.**

Bed

Chair

Desk

Guitar

Wardrobe   Answer...........................

2 **Draw lines to match up each of the following Tudor items with what their owner did.**

Guns and eight hounds	riding
Saddle	had children
Wooden crib	hunting

3 **Look at this inventory showing the possessions of John Cotterell who died in 1572. Then answer the question below.**

Inventory of John Cotterell, Servant
Died 1572.

Barley and wheat	Two pigs
Some land sown with corn	Peas, hay and some oats in the barn
Seven shelves	One bedside cupboard
Some timber	Six sheep
Some money	A chest
Set of clothes	The lease of the house

We know John Cotterell sometimes worked as a servant.

Can you tell what other work he did from looking at the things in his inventory?

Answer ....

ACTIVITY:
Write an inventory of your own bedroom.
You can group things (like 'set of clothes') so you don't have to list everything separately.
Make sure you write down all the important things that say something about what you do.

Life of the Poor

The Tudors believed that only the "deserving poor" should be helped by tax money or charity.
You were "deserving poor" if you were too old, too young or too sick to go to work.

1 **Put each of these types of people into the right column of the table below.**

~~children and babies~~
sick people
healthy adult men
old people
healthy adult women

Deserving Poor — got help	Sturdy beggars — didn't get help
children and babies	

2 **Below is a list of things that affected poor people in Tudor times. Tick the boxes next to things that would have <u>helped</u> poor people.**

☐ Almshouses were built to give old poor people homes.

☐ Begging was made illegal and punished by whipping.

☐ The law said you couldn't stay in a village unless you had a job.

☐ Churches made collections to give to the poor.

☐ Poor orphans were apprenticed — which meant they learnt a trade.

<u>ACTIVITY</u> — HOW DID THE TUDORS ENTERTAIN THEMSELVES?
Use books or the Internet to find out what Tudor people did for fun.

Which of these things do people still do today?
Which things would people not do today? Why?

Health and Hygiene

Tudor doctors didn't know nearly as much about science as doctors do today.

1 | **Below is a list of different medical jobs from Tudor times. Draw lines from each job to match it to what the job was like.**

A midwife was...   ...a person who mixed medicines from their ingredients.

A barber-surgeon was...   ...a doctor who had studied medicine at university.

An apothecary was...   ...a barber who cut off limbs as well as hair.

A physician was...   ...a woman who helped deliver babies.

2 | **Below is a list of cures that were used in Tudor times. Tick the ones that we still use in this country.**

☐ Herbal cures

☐ Blood letting (deliberately making a person bleed)

☐ Putting live leeches onto a person's skin to suck out some blood

☐ Bandages

3 | **Read this passage and answer the question below.**

> Tudor hygiene was very bad. There were no proper sewers.
> Most people emptied chamber pots into the street. Waste was
> also thrown into the river, making the water dirty. This caused
> a disease called typhoid. Without hot running water few
> people had baths regularly. People washed in basins instead.

Name three hygiene benefits that we have and the Tudors did not:

1. ....

2. ....

3. ....

Think how painful operations would have been without anaesthetics. Ouuuuuch.

World War Two

The Second World war lasted for 6 years, from 1939 to 1945.

1 | Read the following passage and draw a circle round the right word from each set of brackets.

On 1st September 1939 Germany, under the (**rule / piano**) of Hitler, invaded Poland. Germany wanted to (**win / give**) back some of the land they lost in World War One. Two (**days / years**) later, on 3rd September, Britain and France declared war on Germany.

Italy joined the Germans and together they started to (**borrow / take over**) many other (**countries / towns**). Two years later in (**1945 / 1941**) Japan attacked the American navy in Pearl Harbour and sank most of their (**ships / planes**). The next day America declared war on (**Britain / Japan**).

2 | Look at the map on the right. The fighting only happened in Europe, around the Pacific and in small parts of Africa. So why was it called a <u>world</u> war?

☐ The fighting happened in countries that weren't England.

☐ All major world powers and many smaller nations were involved.

3 | Look at the timeline. Draw lines to show who were the Allied powers and who were the Axis powers. I've done the first ones for you.

1939 **Britain** and **France** unite to declare war on **Germany**.
1940 **Italy** joins **Germany**.
1941 **Japan** attacks **America**.
1941 **America** declares war on **Japan**.
1941 **Germany** declares war on **America**.
1945 **Germany** and **Japan** surrender.

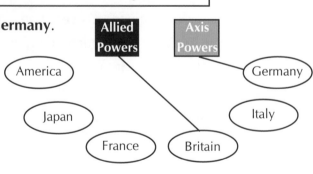

4 | Draw lines to show which leader belongs to which country.

Country	Leader
Britain	Franklin D. Roosevelt
USA	Winston Churchill
Germany	Adolf Hitler

53 million people from many different countries were killed in World War II.

The Blitz

The Blitz began in the summer of 1940 and lasted for a year.

Read the passage below and use it to help you answer the questions on this page.

Almost every night, bombs were dropped on Britain from German planes.
More than 10,000 people died in London alone.
The Germans wanted to make the British people give in.
They also wanted to destroy things that Britain needed for fighting.
In 1939 the British government introduced blackouts, which meant that the German planes couldn't see any lights on the ground.

1 **Circle the places that the Germans would have been trying to destroy in the Blitz.**

Weapons factories   Shipyards
                                              Forests
Sweet shops
        Oil depots   Jewellery shops

2 **Match the beginnings of the sentences below to their correct endings.**

The British blacked out their windows so.......   to protect people from the bombs.

The Government gave out Anderson shelters......   the Germans would not know where to drop the bombs.

The Germans dropped fire bombs.....   to light up the darkness so they could see what they were bombing.

3 **How many people died in the London Blitz? Circle the right answer.**

More than 10,000   1,200

Less than 100   8,768

ACTIVITY:
Imagine you are living in London in 1939.
Write a note to your neighbours explaining why they need to black out their windows.

Food

During the war Britain had trouble getting enough food.
Some of it came from abroad but the Germans kept sinking the ships that delivered it.

1 **There was only a small amount of food to go round so it had to be rationed by the government. What do you think rationing means?** Put a tick next to the right definition.

☐ Giving lots of free food out to everyone.

☐ Selling all the food to the people with the most money.

☐ Limiting the amount people eat so there is enough for everyone.

☐ Frying lots of strips of bacon for everyone.

2 **People were given ration books containing coupons. They needed the coupons to buy food. Here is a list of the rationed food a family would get in a week.**

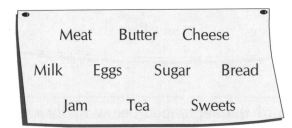

Meat   Butter   Cheese

Milk   Eggs   Sugar   Bread

Jam   Tea   Sweets

If a family wanted more food like potatoes and carrots what was the best way get it?   Put a tick in the box next to the correct answer.

☐ Steal it from their neighbours.

☐ Grow it in their gardens.

☐ Bribe the shopkeeper.

3 **Lots of other items were rationed during the war like coal, petrol, soap, water and clothes. Some items were saved and made into other things to help the war effort. Match the items to the things they were made into.**

Sheets	a baby's cot
Tin cans	gas masks
Drawers	new weapons
Rubber	new clothes

Just be glad you're not wearing clothes made out of pillowcases.

Hardship

There was hardship and suffering for just about everyone during the six years of the war.

1 Men, women and children suffered in different ways. Draw lines to match up the people on the left with the ways of suffering on the right.

Men

Women

Children

All people

some had to work in the factories

many were evacuated — they had to leave home and go to different schools

were frightened and often lost friends, families and homes

those in the army could be hurt or killed while fighting

2 In spite of all the suffering, people tried to stay cheerful. Tick the things that people did to stay cheerful when they were stuck in air raid shelters.

☐ watched television

☐ listened to the radio

☐ played on their PlayStations

☐ sang songs

☐ read and told stories

☐ played outside

ACTIVITY:

Imagine you are a child who was evacuated to the countryside during the war. It is 1945 and the war is over. You have just gone back to school in your town. Your teacher tells you about classmates and friends who were killed during the bombing raids.

Write a diary entry for that day.
Think about how you would feel.

Evacuees

In September 1939 one and a half million children were evacuated from the cities
to the countryside to live with foster parents.

1 | **Why were the children evacuated to the countryside? Tick the correct answer.**

a) Their families didn't want them any more. ☐

b) The children wanted to see the countryside. ☐

c) So that the children would be protected from ☐
the bombs.

2 | **For many of the evacuees it was the first time they had seen the countryside. Shade in the things they would have learnt about there.**

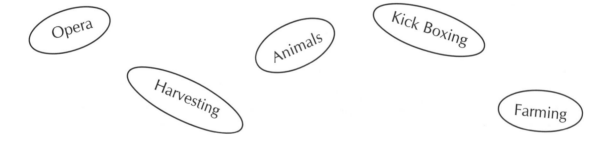

Opera

Animals

Kick Boxing

Harvesting

Farming

3 | **Some children liked their new homes in the countryside but many of them were homesick. Underline the words that describe how the homesick children would have felt.**

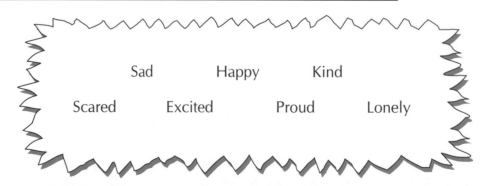

Sad   Happy   Kind

Scared   Excited   Proud   Lonely

Growing up in Britain during the war was hard. Many children never forgot their experiences.

Ancient Egypt

Thousands of years ago the Egyptians built one of the world's first great civilisations.

1 **Look at the timeline below then answer the questions.**

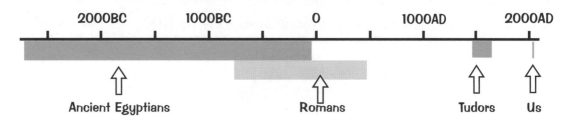

a) Who came first — the Romans or the Tudors?   ....

b) Which is the oldest civilisation on the timeline?   ....

c) Did the Ancient Egyptians overlap with the Romans?   ....

2 **Find the words to do with Ancient Egypt in the wordsearch below.**

V	P	N	I	X	M	A
P	A	P	Y	R	U	S
H	Y	G	Y	U	M	P
A	E	R	U	T	M	H
R	T	K	A	O	Y	I
A	C	N	S	M	I	N
O	H	E	D	B	I	X
H	S	W	R	L	A	D
T	O	O	E	Y	Z	P

SPHINX
TOMB
NILE
PHARAOH
PAPYRUS
MOSES
PYRAMID
MUMMY

The words can be written in any direction, backwards or forwards.

3 **Draw lines to match the sources of information below to what they might tell us about Ancient Egyptian life.**

Sources of information	What they might tell us

pictures and hieroglyphics painted on the walls of an Egyptian king's tomb

the film "The Mummy Returns"

artefacts (things made by people) dug up from the ground where a village once stood

how ordinary people lived

how rich, powerful people lived

nothing — it's a modern made-up story

Quack

Egyptian picture-writing is called "hieroglyphics." Only priests and scribes knew how to write.

Geography of Egypt

Egypt is a hot, dry country in North Africa. Almost no rain falls in Egypt.

1 Look at the picture showing where Ancient Egypt was on the globe. Then answer the questions with YES or NO.

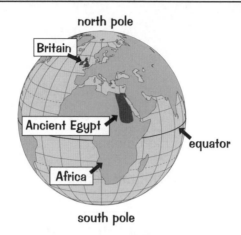

north pole

Britain

Ancient Egypt

equator

Africa

south pole

Is Egypt near the south pole? ....**NO**............

Is Egypt an island? ....

Is Egypt south of Britain? ....

Is Egypt closer to the equator than Britain? ....

2 Circle the correct words in the piece of writing below.

Most of Egypt is hot, dry **MOUNTAINS / DESERT**.
The only part of Egypt where **PYRAMIDS / CROPS**
can grow is on the land near the River Nile. The
Nile stretches for about a thousand **KILOMETRES /
METRES**, running the whole length of Egypt.
In ancient times the easiest and most pleasant way
to travel was by **BOAT / AIRSHIP**.

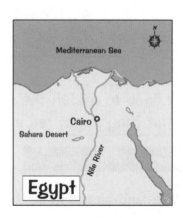

Mediterranean Sea

Cairo

Sahara Desert

Nile River

Egypt

ACTIVITY:
Imagine you went on a time-travel holiday to Ancient Egypt.
Write a postcard to your friends to tell them all about it.
(Hint: Tell them about the weather, the food, the transport, what you saw and who you met.)
You'll need to find out information from books or the Internet.

Nile, Food and Farming

The flooding of the River Nile was important to the Ancient Egyptians.

1 | **The photo shows how the Nile looks today. Use the words below to label the different parts of the landscape.**

CROPS — growing on the flat land by the river.

BOATS — going up and down the Nile.

DESERT — used for burying the dead.

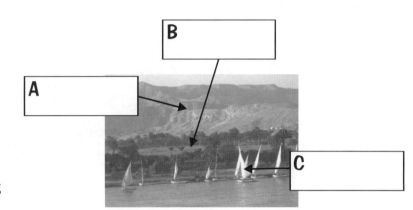

A

B

C

2 | **Some of the words in the passage below are missing. Fill them in from the words in the box.**

Every year the Nile .... Then water spreads over the land for about twenty kilometres each side of the river. The flood water carries with it rich, black .... from the river bed. When the flood dries up the land is left covered with a layer of new .... that was once river-mud. This helps the .... to grow better.

| CROPS | SOIL | FLOODS | MUD |

3 | **Draw lines to join up each thing found in the Nile to the correct description of how it was used.**

FISH   ...were bundled up and used to make boats.

REEDS   ...were caught in nets.

GEESE   ...was dried out and made into bricks.

MUD   ...were hunted with spears by people on boats.

DISCUSSION: *Can you think of any places in the world that have flooded recently?*
Did people think it was good or bad that these places flooded?

Artefacts

The Egyptians built gigantic monuments like the pyramids.
They built them so well that many of them are still around today.

1 **These pictures all show things made by Egyptians. Under each picture write a letter to show which explanation goes with it:**

A The Sphinx is an enormous statue of a lion with a man's head.

B A sarcophagus is a coffin. The Egyptians often made them in the shape of a person.

C The walls of tombs were covered with pictures and hieroglyphics.

D Thousands of labourers and stonemasons built the pyramids.

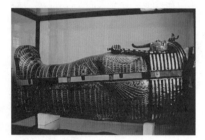

1. ....

2. ....

3. ....

4. ....

2 **Which two artefacts show that the Egyptians were skilled enough to have really big building projects? Write the letters from question 1 in the spaces below.**

1. .... 2. ....·

3 **Artefacts like tools, jewels and furniture found inside the pyramids have survived for thousands of years. Why do you think they have lasted for so long? Circle the likely answers.**

Anything put under a pyramid is kept looking like new by magic spells.

Inside a pyramid, the air is cool and dry. This stops man-made things from rotting.

The artefacts were well hidden inside the pyramids so they were safe from grave robbers.

The pyramids weren't built by magic... just thousands and thousands of Egyptians.

Life After Death

The ancient Egyptians didn't build pyramids and make mummies just for fun.
They did it because they believed that a person would need his or her body in the next life.

1 **Are these things that the Egyptians BELIEVED or that they DID?**

Write **B** for 'believe' or **D** for 'did'.

a) There are powerful gods and goddesses who rule over mankind.

b) After death you still need your body and your possessions.

c) The dead bodies of people, and sometimes cats, were mummified.

d) After death the gods weigh your heart to find out if you have lived a good life.

2 **Write these four sentences below in the right order. Start with the biggest thing.**

This is called a mummy.

Inside the pyramid is a secret room.

Inside that there is a dead body covered with bandages.

Inside that there is a sarcophagus.

Write the sentences in the right order here:

1. ....

2. ....

3. ....

4. ....

3 **Draw lines to match up four Ancient Egyptians with the things an archaeologist might find in each person's tomb.**

Pharaoh — Iron chisel, plumb line, stone hammer.

Stonemason — Papyrus scroll, stone pot for ink, reed pen.

Rich lady — Models of slaves, treasure chest, golden death mask.

Scribe — Stone pot for make-up, bronze mirror, jewellery.

ACTIVITY: _Imagine it was normal for us to be buried with things that we might need in the next life. Make a list of the things you would want to be buried with you._

Answers

Section 1 — The Romans

Page 3

Q1 Choosing to move house: We moved nearer to the best school in the area so we could send our daughter there.
We wanted to live in the countryside, so we moved out of the city.
Forced to move house: There was a war in our village, so we had to move to somewhere safer.
I lost my job, so I had to move to a place where I could get a new job.

Q2 1. Invasion is arriving at an area and attacking it.
2. Settlement is staying in an area for a long time.
3. Emigration is moving away from where you were born.

Q3 i Armour
s Home
s Farming
i War
s Stay
i Conquest

Page 4

Q1 The Romans spoke Latin. — The Celts spoke a language similar to Welsh. D
The Romans were all ruled by one Emperor. — The Celts had many kings. D
The Romans worshipped many gods. — The Celts worshipped many gods. S.
Roman men all shaved. — Celtic men wore moustaches. D
The Romans wore tunics. — The Celts wore trousers. D
Many Romans lived in towns. — The Celts did not have towns. D

Q2 A Celt (Celtic Chief)
Reasons — wearing moustache and trousers.

Q3 R = "Our soldiers join the army for 20 years."
R = "Our army is split up into different legions."
C = "The king is pleased when we win battles."

Q4 The Celts were famous for their Poetry, Metalwork and Jewellery.

Page 5

Q1
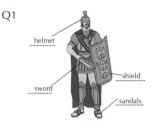
helmet
shield
sword
sandals

Q2 1. The Roman army was split into different sections called legions.
2. There were about 30 legions in the whole Empire.
3. Each legion was made up of 60 centuries.
4. One century contained about 80 men.

Q3 The Romans first invaded England in 55BC. The Britons fought fiercely and drove them back. The Romans invaded again one year later. This time they beat the Britons, but then had to go to France to fight off a rebellion. The Emperor Claudius finally invaded properly almost 100 years later in AD43. This time the Romans were here to stay, and ruled England for nearly 400 years.

Page 6

Q1 a) Iceni
b) He thought it would keep his family safe.
c) The Romans tried to take the fortune Boudicca's husband had left.

Q2 The correct order is B, C, A.

Page 7

Q1 Hypocaust systems were a bit like central heating. A wood-burning furnace was built under the floor. It sent hot air up through the floor and gaps in the walls. The floor was held up by lots of pillars, so the hot air could spread everywhere.

Q2 1. changing room
2. warm room
3. hot steam room
4. cold pool
5. hypocaust

Section Two — The Anglo-Saxons

Page 8

Q1

Eastern Britain
Jutes
Denmark
Angles
Saxons
Saxony

Q2 Raiders take part in a surprise attack, often to steal.
Migrants go to a new country to live there permanently.
Refugees have to flee their own country because of danger.
Settlers go to a country to live there permanently.
Invaders enter another country as enemies, intending to conquer it.

Q3 Peaceful — Migrants, Refugees, Settlers
Warlike — Raiders, Invaders

Page 9

Q1 Fact 1 — Reason C
Fact 2 — Reason D
Fact 3 — Reason A
Fact 4 — Reason B

Q2 Any reasonable answer — e.g.:
1. The Anglo-Saxons built stone churches, some of which still stand.
2. Books written by Christian monks have survived.

Page 10

Q1 1. A 5. H
2. H 6. A
3. H 7. A
4. A 8. A

Q2 You can't dig everywhere. So you do a survey to see where would be a likely place to make interesting finds. An aerial survey can show things invisible when you're on the ground. But the actual excavation isn't so easy. Working by hand using trowels, the archaeologists carefully remove the layers of earth and rock.

Q3 The fort was built first — it has been buried in the ground and the house has been built later on the ground above it.

Page 11

Q1 1. The pictures show a shield and a helmet.
2. They were found at Sutton Hoo.
3. They are made of metal.
4. Anglo-Saxon women did not fight, so they must have belonged to a man.

Q2 Musical instruments and jewellery — Anglo-Saxon life was not all war and fighting.
A sceptre — The dead person was a king.
Some Christian symbols — At that time England was partly Christian and partly not.

Q3 A

Section Three — The Vikings

Page 12

Q1

Sweden
Norway
Denmark
Britain
EUROPE

Q2 Correct Reasons:
- England had good weather and soil for growing crops.
- Scandinavia was very cold and had poor soil for growing crops.
- England had weak defences.

Q3 1. raids
2. Danelaw
3. Yorvik

Answers

Page 13

Q1

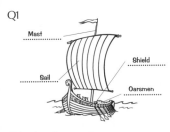

Mast
Shield
Sail
Oarsmen

Q2 longboats, rivers, monasteries
Q3
1. True
2. False
3. False
4. False
5. True

Page 14

Q1 (In any order)
Romans
Anglo-Saxons
The Vikings
The Normans

Q2 AD787   Vikings first visit Britain
     AD793   Vikings raid Lindisfarne
     AD865   Vikings armies invade England

Q3

	Invaded	Left or conquered
Romans	AD43	AD410
Anglo-Saxons	AD400	AD1066
Vikings	AD787	AD1066
Normans	AD1066	

Page 15

Q1 They did:
Read books
Write books
Teach others

Q2 The monasteries were full of gold and silver. T
The Vikings wanted to play football with the monks. F
The monks were peaceful men and would not fight back. T
There were no armies around to defend the monks. T
The monks laughed at the Vikings' boats. F
The monks could be captured and sold as slaves. T
The Vikings did not like the monks' habits. F

Q3 They stole:
Gold
Silver
Tapestries

Page 16

Q1

To protect people from invading armies	To make everyday life easier
Built lots of forts Built a new army Fought bravely in battles Built a new navy	Invented new coins Made new laws Opened schools for children Translated books from Latin so his people could read them

Q2
1. forts
2. an army
3. a navy
Q3 He did many great things while he was King.

Section Four — Henry VIII

Page 17

Q1 Henry was: powerful, clever and selfish.
Q2
a) six
b) no
c) Any reasonable answer — e.g. He wanted a healthy son to rule after him.

Page 18

Q1
a) Henry's counsellors.
b) He became greedy and unpopular, trusted no one, beheaded people and took control of everything.
Q2 hunting
ruling
producing an heir
making money
Q3 Monarch — a ruler with the title King or Queen.
Courtier — a person who is part of the Court.
Tyrant — a cruel and unkind ruler.
Court — all those involved in ruling a country.

Page 19

Q1 The following are true:
Henry had fallen in love with Anne Boleyn.
Catherine gave birth to a daughter but no sons.
Q2 Catherine of Aragon gave him no sons so he married five more times in the hope one wife would have a son. Henry wanted to divorce his wife so he broke away from the Catholic Church, as they did not agree with divorce.

Henry needed more money so he closed down the monasteries and sold all the land.
Q3
1. To get more sons.
2. He wanted to have a wife / companion.

Page 20

Q1 Entertaining the court
Decorating his palaces
Fighting wars
Q2 Correct order is 3, 2, 4, 1
Q3
b) Henry said the monks were lazy and were not following the monastery rules.

Page 21

Q1
a) She was a lady-in-waiting.
b) No
c) He accused her of having an affair and had her beheaded.
Q2
a) She was quiet and did what she was told, unlike Anne Boleyn.
b) Jane had a son.

Page 22

Q1 After Jane's death, one of Henry's advisors suggested that Henry could marry a German princess called Anne of Cleves. That way England and Germany could work together to become very powerful. Henry agreed to marry Anne even though he had only seen a painting of her. When Anne arrived, Henry saw that she was very ugly. He wanted to get out of marrying her, but he could not break his promise to her family. Henry was forced to marry her, but could divorce her quickly as she gave him no children.
Q2 partying
dancing
feasting
singing
Q3 Anne of Cleves — divorced for having no children
Catherine Howard — executed for adultery
Catherine Parr — outlived Henry

Section 5 — Tudor Life

Page 23

Q1
a) poor man
b) rich man
Q2
1. MONARCH
2. NOBLE
3. MERCHANT
4. YEOMAN
5. PEASANT
6. VAGABOND
Q3
a) Latin
b) yes
c) cooking and sewing

Page 24

Q1 Poor houses:
very small garden for vegetables only; no glass in the windows; tiny rooms.
Rich houses:
large kitchen, with space for many cooks; extra rooms for servants to live in; big fireplace; flowers in the garden as well as vegetables and herbs; toilets.
Q2 Carpets from Turkey became popular. — People stopped using rush matting on the floor.
Glass was imported from Venice. — More glass windows in rich and middle-class houses.
There were fewer trees around. — Timber gradually gave way to brick.
Q3 Any reasonable answer — for example:
1. Glass kept draughts out.
2. Carpets were warmer than rush matting.
3. Brick was more solid and kept out draughts.

Page 25

Q1 guitar
Q2 Guns and eight hounds — hunting
Saddle — riding
Wooden crib — had children
Q3 farming

Answers

Page 26

Q1

Deserving poor	Sturdy beggars
Children and babies Sick people Old people	Healthy adult men Healthy adult women

Q2 Almshouses were built to give old poor people homes.
Churches made collections to give to the poor.
Poor orphans were apprenticed — which meant they learnt a trade.

Page 27

Q1 A midwife was *a woman who helped deliver babies.*
A barber-surgeon was *a barber who cut off limbs as well as hair.*
An apothecary was *a person who mixed medicines from their ingredients.*
A physician was *a doctor who had studied medicine at university.*

Q2 We still use —
herbal cures
bandages

Q3 Proper sewers, flushing toilets, hot running water or any other reasonable suggestion.

Section 6 — World War Two

Page 28

Q1 It should read:
On 1st September 1939 Germany, under the rule of Hitler invaded Poland.
Germany wanted to win back some of the land they lost in World War One.
Two days later, on 3rd September, Britain and France declared war on Germany.
Italy joined the Germans and together they started to take over many other countries. Two years later in 1941 Japan attacked the American navy in Pearl Harbour and sank most of their ships. The next day America declared war on Japan.

Q2 All major world powers and many smaller nations were involved.

Q3 Allied Powers — Britain
France
America
Russia
Axis Powers — Germany
Italy
Japan

Q4 Germany — Hitler
Britain — Churchill
America — Roosevelt

Page 29

Q1 Shipyards
Weapons factories
Oil depots

Q2 The British blacked out their windows **so the Germans would not know where to drop the bombs.**
The Government gave out Anderson shelters **so people could be protected from the bombs.**
The Germans dropped fire bombs **to light up the darkness so they could see what they were bombing.**

Q3 More than 10,000

Page 30

Q1 Limiting the amount people eat so there is enough for everyone.

Q2 Grow it in their gardens.

Q3 Sheets — new clothes
Tin cans — new weapons
Drawers — a baby's cot
Rubber — gas masks

Page 31

Q1 **Men** — those in the army could be hurt or killed while fighting
Women — some had to work in the factories
Children — many were evacuated — they had to leave home and go to different schools
All people — were frightened and often lost friends, families and homes

Q3 listened to the radio
sang songs
read and told stories

Page 32

Q1 c) So that the children would be protected from the bombs.

Q2 Farming
Animals
Harvesting

Q3 Sad
Scared
Lonely

Section Seven — Ancient Egypt

Page 33

Q1 a) Romans
b) Ancient Egyptians
c) Yes

Q2

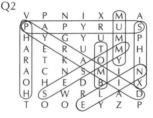

Q3 Pictures and hieroglyphics painted on the walls of an Egyptian king's tomb — how rich, powerful people lived
The film "The Mummy Returns" — nothing — it's a modern, made-up story
Artefacts (things made by people) dug up from the ground where a village once was — how ordinary people lived

Page 34

Q1 Is Egypt near the south pole? No.
Is Egypt an island? No.
Is Egypt south of Britain? Yes.
Is Egypt closer to the equator than Britain? Yes.

Q2 desert, crops, kilometres, boat

Page 35

Q1 A Desert
B Crops
C Boats

Q2 floods, mud, soil, crops.

Q3

FISH ... bundled up... to make boats.
REEDS ...were caught in nets.
GEESE ... made into bricks.
MUD ... hunted them with spears.

Page 36

Q1 1. B
2. C
3. D
4. A

Q2 D and A

Q3 Inside a pyramid, the air is cool and dry. This stops man-made things from rotting.
The artefacts were well hidden inside the pyramids so they were safe from grave robbers.

Page 37

Q1 a) B
b) B
c) D
d) B

Q2 1. Inside the pyramid is a secret room.
2. Inside that there is a sarcophagus.
3. Inside that there is a dead body covered with bandages.
4. This is called a mummy.

Q3

Pharaoh — Iron chisel, plumb line...
Stonemason — Papyrus scroll, stone pot...
Rich lady — Models of slaves, treasure...
Scribe — Stone pot for make-up.